The Lang Arm
o' the Law

The Broons

Since their origin back in 1936, The Broons have had a fair
share of brushes with the law. Whether it be Daphne or Maggie
dating a police sergeant, or Granpaw or Paw getting booked
for an 'honest' misunderstanding. Aye, 10 Glebe Street is no
stranger to a bobbie or two, but everything always works out
for the boys in blue and Scotland's favourite family —
usually anyway.

Oor Wullie

How many times has the wee boy heard the phrase "Name,
address and whaur dae ye bide?" from a certain police
constable? Countless times! The cheeky wee scunner has been
picked up by one PC Murdoch more than the Queen's had
corgis. Poaching, pinching, and picking aipples are just some of
the things listed on Oor Wullie's rap sheet but somehow Wullie
always manages to just stay one step ahead of the lang arm
o' the law, PC Murdoch!

© DCT Consumer Products (UK) Ltd 2020
D.C. Thomson and Co. Ltd,
185 Fleet Street,
London EC4A 2HS

Printed in the EU.

OOR WULLIE

They're Back To Childhood's Happy Day.
You Should Hear What The Neighbours Say!

Oor Wullie's Conscience Let Him Doon,
But Still He Got The Afternoon.

Broon's the name, but ah, which Miss?—
Daph and Maggie don't bank on THIS!

The Broons hae an awfy caper —
Collecting a' the waste paper!

Oor Wullie kens what he's aboot —

That bobby canna catch him oot!

The Roys now live "up on the hill"—

But Maggie Roy's a terror still.

Even on a pitch black night —

Oor Wull just can't keep oot o' sight!

Jim Annan would be a stage sensation
Wi' his animal impersonation!

Wullie's rod is just a gem—
It catches fish and fillets them!

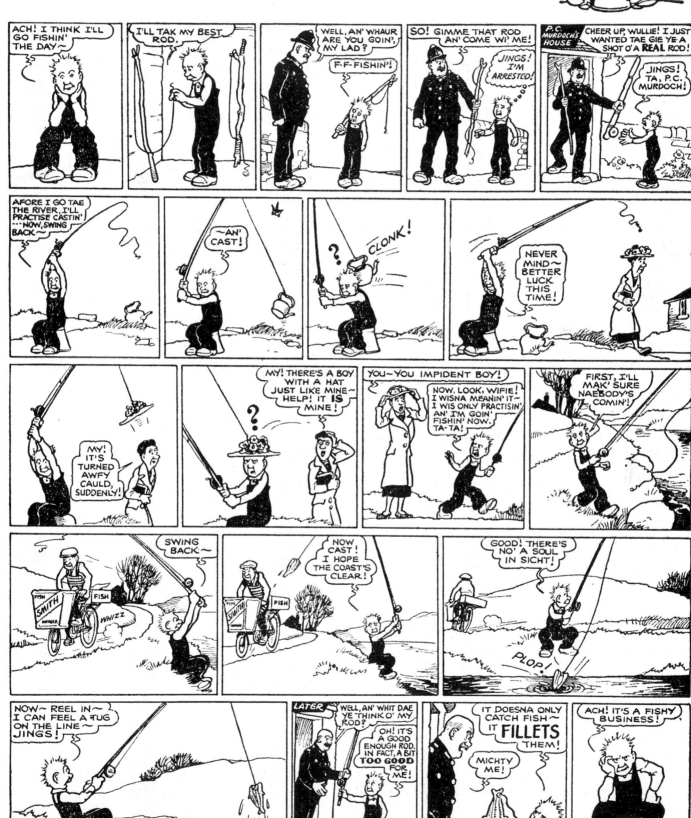

His conscience played a trick on Paw—
There was nae need tae run awa'.

Jings! An' Crivvens! It's no' canny—
Wullie dressed up as a granny.

The bobby hasna a word tae say—
The Bairn points out HE was slidin' tae!

Full speed ahead goes Wullie's cartie—

Carryin' Bob's Pa to a party.

Gran'paw's green-house is a topper—

But he's evicted by a copper!

£999,999 19s 8d mair—

An' Wullie would be a millionaire!

There's pandemonium in the hoose —

A coo-sized dog is on the loose.

Wullie's gettin' awfu' rankled —
That sticky paper's easy fankled.

Paw Broon's in a terrible fix—
It looks like his Daddy's tae give him his licks!

Free air for his ba' was Oor Wullie's need —

A free kick from the bobby — oh, what a dark deed!

Gran'paw's happy Xmas treat —

He packs his things and leaves Glebe St.!

Poor Paw Broon, that unlucky feller —

Thinks Mrs McSpey's a MISFORTUNE-teller!

Wi' mirth see Bob and Soapy rockin'—

The sergeant's knees are fairly knockin'!

Glebe Street's agog with the latest sensation —

Paw Broon's march to the polis station!

Lose the key o' the hoose? No' Paw —

Unless he loses breeks an' a'!

A ba' on a string, some glass and a brick—

Keep Wull and his pals oot o' the nick!

Paw's egg's nae bigger than the rest—

But, by the price, it should be best!

Wullie's ploys keep goin' wrang —

Each time he throws a boomerang.

Whit a disgrace for his kith an' kin—

Gran'paw Broon has been "run in"!

Wullie's swoppin' holus-bolus —

It protects him from the polis!

Whit mak's this sudden change in Paw? —

Twa brushes — one of them wi' the law!

P.C. Murdoch's on his toes,

Makin' sure that Wullie grows!

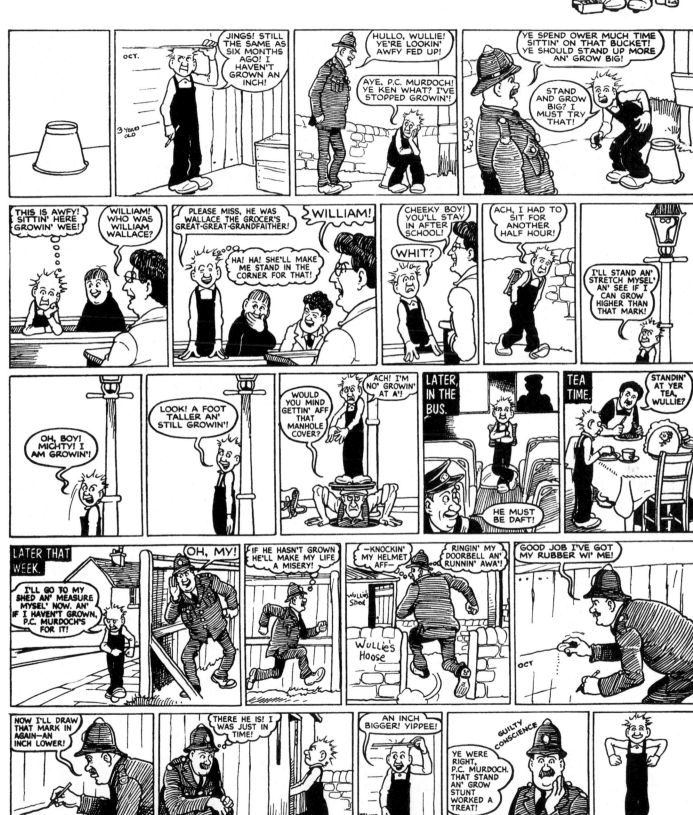

The Broons are up to ninety-nine—

But Granpaw's really doing FINE!

Sandals are nae match for boots!

Or are they? Wullie has his doots!

For Daphne what does the future hold?

She ought to know, for she's been told!

With catapult Oor Wullie's dyin' —

To knock old Murdoch's helmet flyin'!

Television comes to toon—

And plays a trick on Gran'paw Broon!

Wullie the cowboy is the greatest —
His cuddy is the very latest!

Skinny malinky long-legs, umbrella feet—

Hen's in the clutches of a bobby on the beat!

P.C. Wullie Muckle-Feet

Stands no nonsense on his beat!

Poor Paw Broon! He feels a goat—
TWICE on a bus wi' a one pound note!

THREEPENNY ONE PLEASE. SORRY I'VE NAE COPPERS!

THIRTEEN SHILLINGS IN SILVER AN' SIX AN' NINE IN COPPERS!

CHINK! CHINK!

AT HOME

DIDNA HALF GET STUNG THE DAY. I GAVE A CONDUCTOR A POUND AN' GOT 19/9 WORTH O' SMALL CHANGE!

I'M NEEDIN' CHANGE, PAW!

AFTER TEA

GIVE ME CHANGE O' TWA HALF-CROONS!

I'LL DAE THAT A' RICHT. I'VE A POCKETFU' HERE!

PENNIES FOR MA BANKIE!

WE'LL TAK' OOR POCKET MONEY NOW, PAW.

OH, A' RICHT, HERE'S A SHILLIN' EACH!

CHANGE THIS TEN BOB NOTE, PAW!

I COULD DO WI' SOME COPPERS FOR THE PAPERS.

YE'RE WANTED ON THE PHONE, PAW!

TEN BOB O' CHANGE.

SOME COPPERS!

OKAY, TAM! I'LL PUT ON MY BEST JACKET AN' NIP ACROSS RIGHT AWAY.

HEY, WHIT'S THIS? TWA COPPERS AN' A TEN BOB NOTE LEFT.

AYE, AN' YE CAN JUST LEAVE THAT TEN SHILLIN' NOTE FOR THE INSURANCE MAN!

BUS STOP

GIE ME A POST.... I LIKE TAE READ ON THE BUS.

TUPPENNY ONE PLEASE—OH, JINGS! NO! I'VE SPENT MY LAST COPPERS ON THAT PAPER!

SORRY I'VE NAE COPPERS!

YE'LL HAE 238 IN A MINUTE!

229
230
231—

JINGLE! JINGLE!

A'body from shop to smiddy
Knew Murdoch went away — OR DID HE?

Look at Gran'paw—nearly in tears!

Caught in the act after all these years!

For Wullie things are looking black!
P.C. Murdoch's on his track!

NAME: Mr Broon [senior] aka "Granpaw".

HEIGHT: Unknown

WEIGHT: Unknown

HAIR COLOUR: White

EYE COLOUR: Blue

MOUSTACHE COLOUR: White

DESCRIPTION: Bearded, lanky.

Quit smoking 2010. Wears a bunnet.

OFFENCES:

- Disturbing the peace
- Misappropriation o' a telephone box
- Vagrancy o' a' kinds
- Misuse o' a seesaw
- Hoggin' the seesaw when there was bairns waitin'
- Tattie pilfering
- Vegetable vandalism
- Kale kidnapping
- Disorderly conduct o' the usual kind
- Haein' a tipple an bein' in charge o' a penny farthing

NOTES:
Often accompanied by his youngest granddaughter, known only as "the Bairn".
Careful, her bark is aye worse than his, and she's no' feart o' giein' ye a guid

tellin' aff!

Watch Wullie earn the £. S. D.—

He's quick to use his head, you see!

Three tae a bed on visiting day?—

Paw an' Gran'paw find a way!

When Murdoch comes upon the scene—

He's like Oor Wullie's apple—GREEN!

It's no' the lassies! It's no' the men!—

Then who's the burglar at Number Ten?

Paw Broon shouldna be so willing —

to shilly-shally over a shilling!

Murdoch's boobed, that's for sure—

He'll rue that fitba' signature!

The lads have NOT got the gardening bug—

but Gran'paw gets his garden dug!

Wullie finds, to his surprise—

He can't see through his own disguise!

'Keep off the grass', the notice says—

But see the Bairn's clever ways!

These shoes are a painful pair—

But it's Daphne's HEAD that's sair!

Upon the scales Oor Wullie stands—

A 'weighty' problem on his hands!

The auld lads think they've been real cute—

Until they see that 'burglar's' loot!

Oor Wullie learns it's not the time—

To own up to his latest 'crime'!

Oor Wullie's sure he'd land in clink—

If Murdoch was a skinnymalink!

 THIS IS THE DAY I BUY MY SWEETIES!

 HELLO, WULLIE! ACH! IT'S AULD MURDOCH AGAIN!

 HE KENS FINE THIS IS THE DAY I BUY SWEETIES!

 I'LL NIP IN HERE AND BUY THEM, THEN GET OOT AGAIN AFORE HE FINDS ME.

 JINGS! THERE'S TWA WIFIES BEIN' SERVED!

 I KNEW IT! THE AULD SCROUNGER'S HANGIN' AROUND OOTSIDE

 WELL, MRS McKAY— IN FOR YER SWEETIES? NO! THE DOCTOR SAYS I'M TOO FAT— HE'S PUT ME ON A DIET. DIET? THAT'S IT!

 HELLO, WULLIE— FANCY MEETIN' YOU HERE! WHIT HAVE YE GOT TODAY? JELLY BABIES!

 AND YOU'RE NO' GETTIN' ANY! YE'RE OWER FAT, SO I'M PITTIN' YE ON A DIET! IT'S FOR YER OWN GOOD! GASP

 HO-HO! THAT FIXED HIM! FANCY AULD MURDOCH SLIMMIN'— HE'D BE A REAL SKINNY-MA-LINK!

WAIT A MINUTE THOUGH...

 ...IF HE WIS THIN, HE'D BE ABLE TAE CHASE ME THROUGH GAPS IN THE FENCES...

 ...AYE, AND HE'D BE ABLE TO RUN FASTER.

 HE COULD HIDE AHENT TREES.

 JINGS! I WISH I'D NEVER PIT HIM ON A DIET!

 THERE'S ONLY ONE THING FOR IT!

 HI! MISTER MURDOCH!

 HERE! I'VE CHANGED MY MIND! EH?

 FLABBERGASTED!

Here comes trouble—

At the double!

One Christmas stocking, mini-size—

Pulls the wool right o'er Ma's eyes!

IN WULLIE'S BEDROOM.

I'LL BE A GREAT PLAYER WI' THE FITBA' BOOTS I'M GETTIN' FOR CHRISTMAS.

HELP!

CRASH!

WULLIE!

I'VE NAE GLASS TAE MEND IT. YE'LL JUST HAVE TAE SLEEP IN THE SPARE ROOM TONIGHT!

BUT SANTA WINNA—

SANTA! HMPH! I'LL BE SURPRISED IF HE LEAVES YE ANYTHING AFTER THIS!

GOOD! MA'S NO' THERE! NOW'S MY CHANCE!

BUT. WULLIE! DINNA YOU DARE OPEN THAT PARCEL.

BUT, MA— I ONLY WANT THE STRING...

A LIKELY STORY! FANCY TELLIN' LIES ON CHRISTMAS EVE. YE'D BETTER BE GOOD IF YE WANT YOUR STOCKING FILLED!

LATER. WULLIE! HOW MANY TIMES HAVE I TELT YE NO' TAE WRITE ON FENCES?

Dear Sa

I'M SURPRISED AT YE DAEIN' SUCH A THING—

—YE'LL NO' GET MUCH IN YOUR STOCKING TONIGHT IF YE DINNA BEHAVE!

HELLO, DAISY— HAVE YE AN AULD DOLLY'S STOCKIN' YE DINNA WANT?

YES! YOU CAN HAVE THIS ONE.

THANKS! THAT'LL DAE FINE.

SOON BE TIME TO HANG UP MY STOCKIN'!

WELL, I'M AWA' TAE HANG UP MY STOCKIN'!

POOR LADDIE! I HOPE HE'S NO' HANGIN UP THAT! MAYBE WE'VE BEEN TOO HARD ON HIM TODAY!

COME ON— WE'D BETTER GO AND SEE!

UPSTAIRS. HERE— WHIT'S THAT BIT O' WOOL?

LOOK— ONE END'S TIED TAE THE BED IN HIS OWN BEDROOM....

LOOK AT THAT NOTE!

DEAR SANTA, I'M NOT SLEEPING IN THIS BED. FOLLOW THIS BIT OF WOOL

LET'S FOLLOW IT!

SO THAT'S WHAT HE WAS UP TO! WE DIDNA HAVE ANY STRING LEFT IN THE HOOSE, SO HE RATTLED DOON THAT WEE STOCKING!

HE FOUND ME ALL RIGHT! MERRY CHRISTMAS, A'BODY!

Try one or two wee guesses—

Why does he want names and addresses?

See this lad! The feet are Eck's—
But it's Wullie's eyes behind the specs!

It's a 'blue' do, but what d'ye think—

All the Broons are tickled pink!

Nae wonder Wullie's looking glum—
It's prison bars for oor wee chum!

What a disgrace! Chased away—

By the police TWICE in one day!

NAME: Harold "Wee Harry" Wulliumson

HEIGHT: 28cm

WEIGHT: 8kg

HAIR COLOUR: White, sometimes a bit o' a mangy grey, dependin' on whether he's escaped the bath or no'.

EYE COLOUR: Broon

DESCRIPTION: West Highland Terrier.

OFFENCES:

- Disturbing the peace
- Public urination
- Misappropriation o' cheese (often wi' his vertically challenged accomplice: Jeemy the moose)
- Consumption o' stolen goods (sausages)
- Tennis ball theft
- Vandalism o' slippers
- Buryin' slippers an' other stolen goods
- Barkin' at a' hours
- Leavin' muddy pawprints in the Polis Station

NOTES:

Dinnae be soft, he may gie ye they big puppy dug eyes, but deep doon he's a cauld-herted, albeit warm an' fuzzy, criminal o' the sandwich pinchin' kind.

How's this for a TALL story...?

See Wullie's wheezes—

With sudden sneezes!

"Open the door! It's the law!"—

And no one's more tickled than Paw!

The paper from just one wee sweet—

Doesn't half mess up this street!

You'll all agree—just ask the Broons—

There's nothing like the old Scots tunes!

Oor Wullie gets big shocks—

When his mouse sits up and talks!

Black looks in more ways than one—

Come Paw Broon's way when he has some fun!

Well, well, well! You'll never guess—

Why Wullie wants this player's address!

Now the Bairn can spell—

But not very well!

Wullie's in an awfy mess —
Ridin' on his steed, Black Bess!

The day that Paw—

Fell foul o' the Law!

Paw dodges the law—

Till he's let down by Maw!

"P.C. Murdoch, come back soon—

That new bobby gets us doon!"

Paw gets what for—

In this 'cold' war!

Wullie's on the run —

Jings! What has he done?

Paw put the "savings" in a funny place—

Now watch him trying to save his face!

Maybe it is and maybe it's not

the best, the ideal, camping spot!

Black cats bring luck? So they say—

But here's a real cat-astrophe!

Why is Wullie's face sae lang? —

Ach, everything is goin' wrang.

WORRIED PAW, HE FEARS THIS WATTER

MIGHT DESTROY HIS FISH IN BATTER!

Zorro? Batman? Need you ask . . .

. . . who's the lad behind the mask?

DAPH'S TA'EN ON, JOE'S ON THE FLOOR —

IT REALLY IS A FAMILY STORE!

P.C. Murdoch's great, big feet . . .

. . . suffer when he's on the beat.

It's easy tae see —

—— the apple didnae fall far frae the tree!

Oor hero goes the whole hog . . .

. . . tryin' tae train his dog.

Granpaw's early night —
— gies a'body a fright!

The reviews are certainly far fae glowin' . . .

. . . *for Murdoch's voice an' Wullie's bowin'.*

Paw makes sure they keep it down . . .

. . . after their night on the town!

Not a toot comes oot!

HE'S AWA' TAE A JUMBLE SALE . . .

A late-nicht test . . .

. . . tae decide wha's best!

Wullie's no' sae pleased tae meet

the new young Bobby on the beat!

 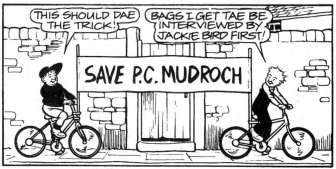

KEN. H. HARRISON.

He tries tae be a naughty lad . . .

. . . but, in truth, he's not ALL bad!

MICHTY ME! THE SHAME! THE SHOCK!

MAW'S BEEN MADE THE LAUGHING STOCK!

A rod frae Wullie's favourite copper

lands oor chum a proper whopper!

Daphne likes a romantic note —
but this one really gets her goat!

NAME: Wullium aka "Oor Wullie"

HEIGHT: 140cm

WEIGHT: 32kg

HAIR COLOUR: Blonde, an' aye spikey, unless his ma's takin' him tae a posh do'

EYE COLOUR: Blue

DESCRIPTION: Wears tackety boots, black dungarees an' a white shirt. Often armed wi' a pea-shooter, catty an' known criminal "Jeemy the moose" in his pocket. Has a bucket. Will sit.

OFFENCES (some of...):

- Impersonating an officer o' the law
- Defamation o' the character o' a certain officer o' the law
- Vandalism concerning an officer o' the law and his "muckle big feeet"
- Running ower the foot o' an officer o' the law in his unlicensed cartie vehicle
- Drivin' a cartie wi'oot a license
- Puttin' a puddock in the hat o' an officer o' the law
- Evading an officer o' the law
- Knocking a polisman's hat aff wi' a catty for the purpose of wearing it
- Knocking a polisman's hat aff wi' a catty for the purpose o' his ain entertainment
- Driving his cartie in a pedestrian zone
- Driving his cartie ower a sergeant's sair feet an' gettin' a certain officer o' the law in trouble for it
- The murderin' o' the sweet music o' bagpipes

NOTES:

A shenaniganiser. Sometimes in disguise or hidin' in aipple trees so keep your eyes peeled.

MURDOCH'S LAW

You micht never guess when ye first meet me that I am a sentimental man. You look at me and see this tough, battle-hardened, modern polis officer (well, maybe no' but I'm working on it). You'd never guess that I'm the sort o' fellah tae hae kept a' his polis notebooks since the day he started work in Auchenshoogle. Sometimes I take them oot and look back at the auld cases. I've been a polisman for a long time, y'ken. Let me read ye this auld entry and see if ye can guess wha I'm talking aboot.

"I was patrolling Stoorie Street when I heard a loud thump followed by the tinkling o' breaking glass and the howling o' an irate person. On entering the gairden o' one Mr Green I found him jumping up and down in fury. Glass from a broken greenhouse window lay on his path and beside it a football. I turned tae calm Mr Green down, lest he do himself a mischief. When I looked back the football was gone and I just caught sight o' a spiky yellow haired head disappearing over the gairden wall." Aye, that was my first glimpse o' the laddie — I hate tae think how many pages o' my notebooks that he has filled since then.

Auchenshoogle is a fine toon and serious crimes are unheard o' — crazy crimes however, are a daily occurrence. The toon has mair than its fair share o' eccentrics, idiots, and jokers. In my time I've been called oot tae investigate fowk juggling yoghurt pots in the supermarket aisle, a mysterious case o' phone boxes filled wi' puddocks, and Mistress McTavish's huge bloomers on her washing line being swapped for polka dot thongs. At Halloween there are aye reports o' supernatural goings-on. I've lost count o' the times I've chased ghosties in the churchyard — ghosties who wear trainers and have Spider-Man sheets ower their heads.

The way tae solve these crimes was not tae go fleeing aboot in a squad car wi' the siren blaring but tae softly walk my beat (as softly as my size 22 polis boots would allow) and listen tae the locals gossiping. They aye had a guid idea o' who did what. Stop in at the local post office and chat tae fowk in the queue. Blether wi' the delivery lads and hae a fish supper at Toni's chipper. That's the way tae find oot who're the goodies and who're the baddies in your toon. When I was on nightshift I liked tae look intae the Auchenshoogle Bakery. The smell o' fresh baked bread made your mooth water and I aye had a couple o' warm mince rolls. MacDougall the baker liked tae get all the news and I liked tae watch his daughter Millicent knead the dough. She had the highland beauty o' Flora McDonald and the arms o' a highland blacksmith. Man, she could batter that dough intae shape. On Mondays I would escort her tae the bank wi' the weekend monies, in case she met a robber, y'understand. Soon though, I was escorting her on romantic walks on oor days off. One time a local comedian asked if I had the handcuffs on her. I said nothing but Millicent's swinging handbag knocked him intae Pranny Pond. What a laugh we had. She felt safe wi' me. (I felt safer wi' her around as well).

Oor wedding was a grand affair, only one invite was sent oot — inviting the whole o' Auchenshoogle tae the Co-operative Hall. I played the pipes mysel' and Millicent led the dancing — man it was wild! One o' the eightsome reel sets ended up in casualty — well they did try tae birl Millicent aff her feet. There was nae fancy wedding breakfast just mince rolls all roond. Mr MacDougall was aye the businessman. When we left tae go on honeymoon I threw coins tae the youngsters waiting by the taxi, a scramble it was kent as. This was the custom back then. The wee lad wi' yellow spiky hair pushed and shoved and dived and fought and near got a' the cash. You ken who I mean.

We moved intae the polis hoose which pleased Millicent as it had a braw big gairden and she liked tae grow flooers. It was a time o' joy — everything was just tickety-boo. Until the day a dark cloud descended on us all. A new polis sergeant was moved tae the town, Sergeant Herbert Cramond. The powers that be had decided that Auchenshoogle's polis force (me) needed tae be modernised. So they sent us this hot-shot sergeant who had never been oot o' the city. He was going tae make oor town crime-free and if I didn't back him up I would be sacked. I could tell you Sergeant Cramond was obnoxious, mean, twisted, cruel, and really up his own bahoochie but that makes him sound decent. He was worse than that. For the first week, Cramond never came oot o' the office. He pulled all the reports and files and studied them.

He only stopped tae shout at me for sitting doon. What was I tae do? Write his blessed reports standing up? Yes was his answer.

All this studying eventually led tae him revealing his big plan. I had been lazy and had let one major criminal run loose. His crimes were playing football in the street, fishing where fishing was not permitted, climbing park trees which was against park by-laws, playing truant from school, and, last but not least, breaking greenhoose windows wi' a catapult. Various witnesses, namely one Grumpy Green, had described the villain as being small wi' spiky yellow hair. This criminal must be stopped at all costs or heads would roll — mine!

Wi' my extensive knowledge o' Auchenshoogle, I was aware o' the whereabouts o' the yellow spiky haired criminals' lair. It was his shed in his back gairden. He was feeding his pet moose when I shoved my way in after school that evening. His so-called criminal ways were easy tae change. I wid put up a real goal wi' a net in the park tae stop him playing football

in the street. I'd get him intae the Angling Club where he micht catch salmon instead o' tiddlers in the castle loch. Forget climbing trees in the park, the climbing wall at the sports centre was twice as difficult. Playing truant? "Stop it or I'll tell your faither." The only thing I couldn't get him tae stop was firing his beloved catapult. If I confiscated it he just made another one. I didn't want this wee laddie tae fall intae Cramond's clutches. It was a problem I took home tae the tea table that night. Millicent, who was ever practical, said that this laddie needed something more exciting tae fire his catapult at than boring old Grumpy Green's windows. She was richt o' course and I had a notion that might just work. Next day in the polis lost and found department, I looked oot the old London bobby's helmet that had been lying there since the last century. I put it on and it suited me fine. Sergeant Cramond howled wi' rage saying it was against regulations but when I explained that my head was needing more air for my brain was overheating wi' all his orders, he just growled. "You are a clown, so look like one."

Wearing the helmet I went oot on my beat. The first catapult shot knocked off my helmet at the corner o' Bridge Street. By the time I cleared High Street it had been knocked off twice more. And yes, I had spotted the spiky yellow haired boy. But no windows were broken that nicht — he had found a much more exciting target. Cramond was happy as his so-called crime figures were down. I went about my beat and he didn't bother me

much. Too busy crowing how he had tamed Auchenshoogle.
It was on one o' these quiet nights that a report came in about an escaped tiger being spotted in the supermarket car park. Sensing glory, Cramond took control. A SWAT team was called in and press and TV were informed.

The tiger did appear, only it was wagging its tail and sniffing the bins. It was the big soft dug from the hotel wearing a paper tiger mask and a tiger pattern duvet cover over its back. I had seen that duvet cover before — in the yellow spiky haired boy's gang hut. Lots o' people had their phones and the whole hilarious incident was filmed many times. It went viral — almost everyone in the world had seen it and laughed. Cramond was a laughing stock and blushed for about a week. Whenever he tried tae boss me about I'd just growl like a tiger and he'd dash off.

I'm still on duty in Auchenshoogle but realise I've become a bit o' a legend. The only polisman in Scotland wi' a London bobby's helmet. My size 22s are the biggest feet in the force. And I often play my bagpipes as I plod along my beat. It's like a polis car siren and abody kens I'm on my way. I continue tae outsmart that creative wee rascal wi' the yellow spiky hair but I think both you and I know I'll never win that one. Just look at some o' my most recent cases and you'll agree.

Yours,

PC Murdoch

PC MURDOCH MYSTERIES SAIR FEET

PC MURDOCH MYSTERIES UNDERCOVER

OOR WULLIE'S

BIG Bucket Trail

Oor Wullie's BIG Bucket Trail was Scotland's first ever nationwide public art trail. Starting on the 17th of June, 2019, the trail ran for a massive eleven weeks, attracting people from around the globe as over 1.5 million people visited the sculptures. Fans of the dungaree-clad scamp could visit locations all over Scotland where more than 200 statues of Oor Wullie on his bucket were displayed on the streets, in galleries, transport stations, and other public spaces. Each statue was individually designed and hand-painted. Some statues were painted to depict specific themes such as recycling and protecting nature, while others were created as homages to celebrities and famous characters, including, of course, PC Murdoch!

After several farewell events and the auctioning of the statues, the BIG Bucket Trail raised £1.29 million for Edinburgh Children's Hospital, Glasgow Children's Hospital and the Archie Foundation.

NOO THAT'S WHIT I CALL TRAILBLAZIN' TAE RAISE BUCKETS O' CASH FOR GUID CAUSES!

It's been over eighty years since their Fun Section debut in The Sunday Post, and while the laws might have changed, one thing remains the same: The Broons and Oor Wullie are never far from the reach o' the lang arm o' the law!

And so, it may have taken eight decades, but Auchentogle and Auchenshoogle's favourite polisman (how large is his beat?!) finally got the respect he was due and a strip of his own. But what does the future hold for these crude criminals and juvenile jailors? Never fear, mischief is always close at hand where The Broons and Oor Wullie are concerned!